MODERN BRITAIN

Introduction

The world in which we live is constantly changing. In fact, it always has. Man has consistently reached for developments and inventions that can better our lifestyle and environment. From the earliest invention of the wheel, up to the present day of the internet and wireless communications, the things we use in our day to day lives are forever changing and improving. Some of the things you will I-Spy in this book are all around, others are small things that you may use all the time, but not even notice. Huge structures, such as football stadiums or modern buildings are now taken for granted, as is the internet or an in-car Sat Nav. Modern Britain Britain is not just about buildings and structures – the way we power our homes and dispose of rubbish is also changing. One of the key events over the next few years will be the 2012 Olympic Games, and the buildings, infrastructure and communications needed for this global event will soon be more evident in many places in and around London. Some of the things are more difficult to Spy than others so, if you are going on a journey or on holiday, why not find out what there is to go and see. But keep your eyes open, Modern Britain is all around!

How to use your I-SPY book

As you work through this book, you will notice that the subjects are arranged in groups which are related to the kinds of places where you are likely to find things. You need 1000 points to send off for your I-Spy certificate (see page 64) but that is not too difficult because there are masses of points in every book. As you make each I-Spy, write your score in the box and, where there is a question, double your score if you can answer it. Check your answer against the correct one on page 63.

I-SPY TITLES AVAILABLE:

- Ancient Britain
- At the Airport
- At the Seaside
- Birds
- Camping
- Car Badges
- Cars
- Classic Cars
- Creepy Crawlies
- Flags
- Green Britain
- History
- In the Garden
- In the Street
- London
- Modern Britain
- Nature
- On a Car Journey
- On a Train Journey
- On the Motorway
- Sports and Games
- Trees
- Wild Flowers
- Working Vehicles

MILLENNIUM WHEEL

The Millennium Wheel, also known as the London Eye, was erected beside the River Thames in London in 1999. It is 135m (443ft) high and is the largest Ferris wheel in Europe.

I-SPY points: 15

Date: _____

ANGEL OF THE NORTH

Towering over the Tyne and Wear countryside, the Angel of the North is a modern steel sculpture by Antony Gormley. The angel's wings are 54 metres (178 ft) across and the sculpture is 20 metres (66 ft) high.

Which road does the Angel of the North overlook?

I-SPY points: 20
Double with answer

Date: _____

3

O2 ARENA

The O2 Arena began life as the Millennium Dome, the great exhibition centre that was built for the Millennium Experience exhibition of 2000. It is sited on the Greenwich Peninsula in south-west London.

I-SPY points: 15

Date: _____

THAMES BARRIER

The Thames Barrier protects London from tidal surges that might flood the capital. It was built between 1974 and 1982. When weather forecasters predict that high tides or storm surges might cause high water levels in the River Thames, the barriers are closed.

I-SPY points: 20

Date: _____

SEVERN BRIDGE

There are two road bridges that cross the Severn River between England and Wales, which carry over 25 million vehicles a year.

I-SPY points: 15

Date:

EDEN PROJECT

The giant domes of the Eden Project in Cornwall house many exotic plants and trees from around the world. The domes are made up of hexagonal plastic panels, and tubular steel frames. The project includes the world's largest greenhouse.

I-SPY points: 25

Date:

5

SPINNAKER TOWER, PORTSMOUTH

The shape of the Spinnaker Tower in Portsmouth, which is modelled on a wind-filled sail, pays tribute to the city's maritime heritage. Built of steel, it is 170m (559ft) tall.

I-SPY points: 20

Date:

SKYE ROAD BRIDGE

Until 1995, the only way to reach the Isle of Skye in the Scottish highlands was by ferry. The elegant, arched bridge is actually in two parts, as one pillar stands on the small island of Eilean Ban.

I-SPY points: 35

Date:

HINDU TEMPLE

Hindus worship in temples that are often decorated with images of the god to which they are dedicated. People must remove their shoes before entering. The largest temple in Britain is the Shri Venkateswara temple in Tividale.

I-SPY points: 15

Date: _____

MOSQUE

Mosques, where Muslims come together to pray, can also be found in many cities. They often have beautiful domes and towers (called minarettes).

I-SPY points: 15

Date: _____

COVENTRY CATHEDRAL

After the Second World War, Coventry Cathedral was rebuilt on the ruins of the medieval building that had been destroyed by air raids.

I-SPY points: 20

Date: _____

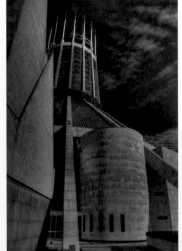

LIVERPOOL CATHOLIC CATHEDRAL

Liverpool Metropolitan Cathedral of Christ the King is a striking modern cathedral that was consecrated in 1967. It has a conical shape and a lantern tower of stained glass.

What is the local nickname for the cathedral?

I-SPY points: 15

Double with answer

Date: _____

GHERKIN (SWISS RE BUILDING)

The Gherkin, more properly called the Swiss Re building, was opened in the City of London in 2004. At 180m high (591ft), this curved glass and steel building is visible from many miles away

What is the address of the Gherkin?

I-SPY points: 15

Double with answer

Date:_____

LIVERPOOL ANGLICAN CATHEDRAL

This is the largest cathedral in the UK and the fifth in the world. This Gothic style cathedral was started in 1904 and finished in 1978.

I-SPY points: 15

Date:_____

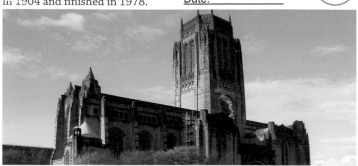

SELFRIDGES BUILDING, BIRMINGHAM

Covered in shiny aluminium discs, the curvy and eye-catching Selfridges Building in Birmingham is a fine example of 'blobitecture'.

I-SPY points: 15

Date: _____

ANTONY GORMLEY'S *Another Place* CROSBY

The beach at Crosby, north of Liverpool is inhabited by over 100 cast iron figures by the sculptor Antony Gormley. They are part of an art installation entitled *Another Place*. The sculptures all face out to sea.

I-SPY points: 25

Date: _____

LLOYDS BUILDING LONDON

Sometimes known as the 'inside-out building', because all the pipes and staircases are on the outside of the structure, the Lloyds Building in the City of London was completed in 1986. On the 11th floor, this 20th century building houses an original 18th-century dining room, carefully transferred from a much older Lloyds building.

What is the address of the Lloyds Building?

I-SPY points: 15

Double with answer

Date: _____

CANARY WHARF

One Canada Square is the tallest building in the UK and was originally named Canary Wharf Tower when it was built in 1991. It is 235.1m (774ft) high. It has featured in many films and TV shows, including *Dr Who* and *Johnny English*.

I-SPY points: 10

Date: _____

MILLENNIUM BRIDGE, LONDON

When it opened in 2000, this pedestrian suspension bridge over the River Thames was nicknamed the 'Wobbly Bridge' because it swayed under the weight of the crowds that flocked to see it.

I-SPY points: 15

Date: _____

TATE MODERN

This museum of modern art is housed in a building that began life in 1947 as the Bankside Power Station.

Which architect, also the designer of the red telephone box, designed the original building?

I-SPY points: 15
Double with answer

Date: _____

CITY HALL - MAYOR OF LONDON'S OFFICE

This bulbous building, which stands on the south bank of the River Thames next to Tower Bridge, is the headquarters of the Greater London Assembly. Its rounded shape helps improve energy efficiency.

I-SPY points: 15

Date:

SCOTTISH PARLIAMENT

In 2004 Queen Elizabeth II opened the new Scottish Parliament building in Edinburgh. The uneven roof line is supposed to remind viewers of the crags in the mountainous Scottish landscape.

I-SPY points: 25

Date:

NATIONAL ASSEMBLY FOR WALES

Constructed of sustainable materials (including over 1,000 tonnes of Welsh slate) and sited in Cardiff Bay, the National Assembly for Wales was opened in 2006. With a vast glass front, it houses a huge mushroom-shaped cowl inside, which uses the wind to ventilate the building.

What is the Welsh name of the building?

I-SPY points: 25

Double with answer

Date: _____

WALES MILLENNIUM CENTRE

Probably more famous to TV viewers as the backdrop to *Torchwood*, the Millennium Centre in Cardiff is home to the Welsh National Opera. Its striking front bears an inspirational message in English and Welsh, 'In These Stones Horizons Sing'.

I-SPY points: 20

Date: _____

WIMBLEDON LAWN TENNIS CLUB

One of the oldest tennis clubs in the world, the Centre Court was always vulnerable to the weather during the annual All-England Tennis Championships. A retractable roof was installed in 2009, which allows play to continue in the rain or after dark.

I-SPY points: 15

Date: _____

LONDON MARATHON

Many big cities host annual marathons through their streets. In London, the 26-mile course starts in Greenwich and ends on The Mall.

Where did the very first marathon take place?

I-SPY points: 10
Double with answer, 10 points for any other city marathon

Date: _____

LONDON 2012 OLYMPIC AND PARALYMPIC GAMES

The Olympic Games have not been held in the UK since 1948! Planning for the London 2012 Games began after London won the bid to stage them in 2005. With state-of-the-art stadiums and arenas, they promise to be a magnificent spectacle.

I-SPY points: 20 for any other Olympic site

OLYMPIC STADIUM

I-SPY points: 20

Date: _____

AQUATICS CENTRE

I-SPY points: 20

Date: _____

OLYMPIC VILLAGE

I-SPY points: 20

Date: _____

ETON COLLEGE ROWING CENTRE

I-SPY points: 20

Date: _____

BASKETBALL ARENA

I-SPY points: 20

Date: _____

WEYMOUTH SAILING

I-SPY points: 20

Date: _____

WEMBLEY

Wembley Stadium, in north London, is the second-largest stadium in Europe and the most expensive football stadium ever built. It cost £798 million and contains 2,618 toilets – more than any other venue in the world!

I-SPY points: 20

Date: _____

CARDIFF MILLENNIUM STADIUM

Opened in Cardiff in 1999, the Millennium Stadium is the national stadium of Wales and home to both the Welsh rugby and football teams. It also hosts rock concerts, other music and sporting events and has a retractable roof.

I-SPY points: 20

Date: _____

EMIRATES STADIUM

Emirates Stadium is home to one of London's oldest football clubs, Arsenal. It was opened in 2006 and replaced the old Highbury stadium.

What is the nickname of Arsenal Football Club?

I-SPY points: 20
Double with answer

Date: _____

I-SPY points: 20
for any other modern
football stadium

Date: _____

CITY OF MANCHESTER STADIUM

Opened in 2002 for the Commonwealth Games, the City of Manchester Stadium, also known as Eastlands, has been home to Manchester City football club since 2003.

I-SPY points: 20

Date: _____

SURFING/ BODYBOARDING

Wetsuits offer protection from the chilly waters of the British coast, and keep surfers warm even in the cooler months.

I-SPY points: 10

Date:

ICE SKATING AT MANMADE ICE RINK

The installation of manmade outdoor ice rinks in many cities in December has brought this particular winter sport to a wider audience.

I-SPY points: 10

Date:

HEELYS

Heelys are trainers with wheels – watch out for children speeding towards you in shopping malls!

I-SPY points: 15

Date:

EXERCISE TRAIL

Many parks and woodlands have installed exercise trails. Runners can vary their exercise routine by using the course while out jogging.

I-SPY points: 20

Date:

INDOOR SKI SLOPE

Thousands of British skiers practise skiing and snowboarding in artificial snow domes or on artificial dry ski slopes. The temperature in the snow dome is always cold, even in summer!

I-SPY points: 25

Date:

PROTECTIVE PADS

Skaters and skateboarders often wear protective pads on their knees and elbows to protect themselves from grazes and scratches if they fall over.

I-SPY points: 5

Date:

BIKE TRAIL

Many disused railway lines have been converted to safe, car-free bike trails. In some woods or hills, there are more tricky bike trails designed for mountain bikes.

I-SPY points: 10

Date:

ROLLER BLADES

Roller blades or inline skates made roller-skating cool and faster. Look out for skaters gliding through parks and open spaces often at high speeds.

I-SPY points: 5

Date:

SILVER SCOOTER

These lightweight, shiny aluminium scooters with small wheels are great for stunts. They fold up easily, so you can take them anywhere.

I-SPY points: 5

Date:

CYCLING HELMET

In some countries it is illegal to ride your bike without a helmet. It is generally safer to wear a helmet when riding on the road.

I-SPY points: 5

Date:

GRAFFITI ART

Graffiti can ruin a building, but occasionally, it is colourful and witty. The most famous graffiti in Britain is by the street artist Banksy.

I-SPY points: 5,
40 points for a Banksy

Date: _____

SKATE PARK

Skateboarders appreciate a variety of concrete surfaces to show off their skills. Purpose-built skate parks are often built near playgrounds or in urban spaces.

I-SPY points: 5

Date: _____

ST PANCRAS STATION

St Pancras is one of London's main stations. Its magnificent Victorian facade hides a huge glass and steel train shed, which is now home to the high speed Eurostar trains.

St Pancras appears in the Harry Potter films. What is the name of the train the young wizards catch?

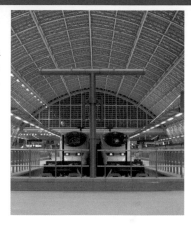

I-SPY points: 10

Double with answer

Date: _____

HEATHROW EXPRESS

The UK's busiest airport, Heathrow is 15 miles from central London. The Heathrow Express connects travellers to the city on a fast new train link.

I-SPY points: 10

Date: _____

CHANNEL TUNNEL

Although people had talked about linking Britain with Europe since 1802, it was not until 1994 that the Channel Tunnel opened. At 50km, it is the longest undersea tunnel in the world, with the section under the sea stretching to 38km.

I-SPY points: 15

Date: _____

EUROSTAR™ TRAIN

Since the completion of the Channel Tunnel, it has been possible to travel between London and mainland Europe in just over two hours on a fast direct train.

I-SPY points: 15

Date: _____

ELECTRIC BIKE

Fitting a motor to a bicycle is a great way to give your bike a speed boost. Many people appreciate the ability to travel a little bit faster without pedalling, especially up hills!

I-SPY points: 15

Date: _____

FOLD-UP BIKE

Fold-up bicycles are specially designed with light aluminium frames to fold-up easily so that they can be carried on trains or into buildings.

I-SPY points: 15

Date: _____

DOCKLANDS LIGHT RAILWAY

The Docklands Light Railway (DLR) opened in 1987 and is unusual in that none of the trains have drivers! It is operated by an automatic train control system. The railway is being expanded to meet the demands of the 2012 Olympics.

I-SPY points: 10

Date: _____

RICKSHAW

Long used in Asia, rickshaws are now popular in many European cities. They are an environmentally friendly method of getting around.

I-SPY points: 15

Date:

OYSTER CARD

Electronic tickets, such as London's Oyster card, mean that passengers spend less time queuing for tickets. The card is swiped over a circular card reader, which activates a ticket barrier and lets the passenger through. The name hints at the phrase, 'the world's your oyster', meaning that you can travel wherever you like. Don't forget to swipe out when you finish your journey.

I-SPY points: 5

Date:

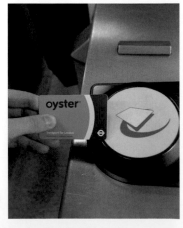

TILTING TRAIN

Tilting trains are able to travel at speeds up to 300km/h (186mph) on regular train tracks, rather than expensive, purpose-built high-speed tracks. Passengers are unaware of the tilting motion as the train speeds around bends.

I-SPY points: 20

Date: _____

BENDY BUS

Bendy buses are longer than traditional buses and can therefore transport a greater number of passengers. You can spot them in London and many cities and airports – and it's great to watch them bend in half as they go round corners!

I-SPY points: 5

Date: _____

AUTOMATIC TICKET BARRIER

Railway stations have used turnstiles to restrict the flow of passengers on to trains for over 100 years. Today, they are electronic, and open once they have 'read' the electronic strip on a passenger's ticket. They can also be found at theme parks, public toilets, museums and many entertainment venues.

I-SPY points: 5

Date: _____

DIGITAL BUS STOP

Digital bus stops, or 'smart stops' have removed some of the frustration of waiting for the bus. An electronic computer-based system plots the bus's position and predicts how long it will take to arrive at the bus stop.

I-SPY points: 10

Date: _____

SPEED CAMERA

Speed cameras record the speed of your car and take a photo of the number plate if you are travelling too fast. You can expect a speeding ticket a few days later in the post!

I-SPY points: 5

Date:

ROADSIDE POLLUTION MONITOR

A pollution monitor can measure and record a wide range of pollutants in the air caused by traffic or even crops.

I-SPY points: 15

Date:

DIGITAL TRAFFIC SIGN ON MOTORWAY

Digital signs are controlled from a traffic control centre and warn motorists of traffic jams or delays further up the road.

I-SPY points: 5

Date:

BMW C1-200 MOTORBIKE

Is it a car or is it a motorbike? The BMX C1-200 has a roof to shelter riders from the rain, and more importantly to provide protection in the event of a crash. These bikes offer the convenience of riding a motorbike but with better protection.

I-SPY points: 10

Date: _____

TERMINAL 5 HEATHROW

The newest terminal at London's Heathrow airport opened in 2008. The main building is the largest free-standing structure in the UK and cost over £4 billion to complete.

I-SPY points: 15

Date: _____

GAS-POWERED BUS

Gas powered buses are visible in some cities. They are environmentally friendly, as they do not produce noxious exhaust fumes.

I-SPY points: 10

Date: _____

TRAM

At the beginning of the 20th century, most British cities had a tram system. They were gradually replaced with buses, but 100 years on, trams are making a comeback and are good tourist attractions.

I-SPY points: 10

Date: _____

ELECTRIC/HYBRID CAR

Fuel for petrol-driven cars is expensive and in increasingly short supply, so car manufacturers are designing new fuel-efficient vehicles powered by alternative fuels, such as electricity, liquefied petroleum gas (LPG).

I-SPY points: 20

Date: _____

LPG REFUELLING POINT

More and more petrol stations provide LPG (liquefied petroleum gas) refuelling points, sometimes called 'autogas'. It is popular with motorists because it is a much cheaper fuel than petrol.

I-SPY points: 5

Date:

ELECTRIC CAR CHARGING POINT

Electric cars are much more environmentally friendly and are becoming more popular.

I-SPY points: 25

Date:

33

CONGESTION CHARGE

Brought in to some cities to reduce the volume of traffic.

I-SPY points: 10

Date: _____

LOW EMISSION ZONE

To keep the air cleaner in the cities.

I-SPY points: 10

Date: _____

SOLAR POWERED BUS STOP

The sun charges the light at the bus stop.

I-SPY points: 10

Date: _____

WIND TURBINE

Wind turbines convert the energy of the wind into electricity. They are always sited in windy places, such as hill tops or out at sea, where there is a strong likelihood of constantly high winds.

I-SPY points: 10

Date: _____

WIND-UP RADIO/ TORCH

Radios and torches powered by a hand-turned crank do not require batteries or mains electricity to operate them. A few minutes spent winding up the mechanism produces hours of use.

Which British inventor designed the first wind-up radio?

I-SPY points: 5
Double with answer

Date: _____

36

WOODBURNING STOVE

Real log fires send 80% of their heat up the chimney. The warmth from a wood-burning stove is projected into the room, and the wood they burn is a renewable resource.

I-SPY points: 10

Date: _____

WATER METER

It is important to conserve water and water meters help us to gauge how much we are using in the home.

I-SPY points: 10

Date: _____

SOLAR PANELS

Solar panels absorb energy from the Sun's rays and convert it into electricity.

I-SPY points: 10

Date: _____

RECYCLING BOX

Most of us sort our rubbish every week and pull out newspapers, bottles, cans and plastics for recycling in special containers.

I-SPY points: 5

Date: _____

REUSABLE CARRIER BAG

Plastic carrier bags are cheap, but after they are thrown away, they will clog up rubbish sites for many years. Many shops now give out stronger, reusable bags, which shoppers are encouraged to use instead of disposable bags.

I-SPY points: 5

Date: _____

RECYCLING CENTRE

Recycling centres, or 'tips' collect and sort household junk. Anything that is broken or just too big for the bin can be taken to a recycling centre – and sometimes you might just find something else that you can use!

I-SPY points: 10

Date: _____

38

ENERGY EFFICIENCY STICKER

Stickers on electrical household items such as washing machines or fridges, let buyers know whether the item uses energy efficiently.

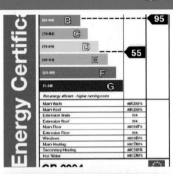

I-SPY points: 5

Date: _____

HOME ENERGY MONITOR

These small monitors display the cost of household electricity usage. Watch the numbers soar every time you switch on a kettle or the oven! It usually reminds everyone to turn off lights, TVs and games consoles.

I-SPY points: 10

Date: _____

LOW-ENERGY LIGHTBULB

Energy-saving lightbulbs use up to 80% less energy than traditional lightbulbs, but produce the same amount of light and generally last for much longer.

I-SPY points: 5

Date: _____

ALLOTMENT

Home-grown fruit and vegetables are delicious. Allotments, small patches of land that people can rent in order to grow their own produce, have become popular again in recent years. They provide both food and recreation.

I-SPY points: 10

Date:

WORMERY

Many people turn vegetable and garden waste into compost, and worms in the compost help break down the materials quickly. Special wormeries can be purchased, with worms that process rubbish leaving behind rich, organic compost for the garden.

I-SPY points: 15

Date:

FESTIVAL POSTER

Every summer there are a number of outdoor music festivals around Britain. People enjoy camping at the festival site to listen to the music all day long.

I-SPY points: 15

Date:

FLORAL TENT

Tents are now available in lots of funky colours and patterns – much more fun than the old green canvas that was once so common.

I-SPY points: 15

Date:

POP UP TENT

As well as being more colourful, tents are now really easy to put up – some are made with springy poles that pop into shape as soon as they're out of the bag!

I-SPY points: 10

Date:

SCENTED CANDLES

Scented candles make your home smell lovely. Some, such as citronella candles, are useful outside as their scent wards off insects.

I-SPY points: 5

Date:_____

CHIMINEA

Chimeneas are popular in gardens in the summer. They can be used as barbecues, or as an outdoor fire to keep out the chilly evening air.

I-SPY points: 15

Date:_____

GLOWSTICKS

Plastic tubes that produce a lovely glow once cracked in half, glowsticks are very popular at after-dark entertainments. They are also used by campers and anywhere a non-flammable, non-electrical light source is needed.

I-SPY points: 10

Date: _____

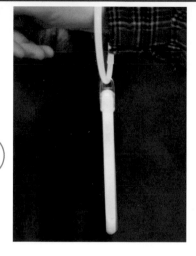

FLORAL WELLIES

Wellington boots were once available in any colour, as long as it was green or black. These days, gorgeous stripes and floral patterns have made wellies trendy.

I-SPY points: 15

Date: _____

PATIO HEATER

Patio heaters are often seen
outside restaurants and can
be used outside to keep decks
and patios warm. They use up
a lot of energy, and are not
environmentally friendly.

I-SPY points: 15

Date: _____

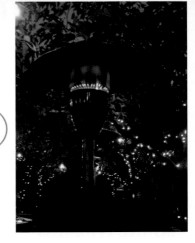

SPA/JACUZZI (OUTDOOR)

Outdoor spas full of warm
bubbling water are a lot of fun,
whatever the weather!

I-SPY points: 20

Date: _____

READY MEAL

Ready meals are great for those who are too busy to cook. They offer a quick, tasty meal that can be ready within minutes.

I-SPY points: 5

Date: _____

ENERGY DRINK

Energy drinks claim to improve drinkers' alertness or physical performance. They generally contain caffeine, sugar and other flavourings and herbs designed to give them a great taste.

I-SPY points: 5

Date: _____

BOTTLED WATER

Bottled water is available almost everywhere, but it is better for the environment if you refill a reusable bottle with tap water.

I-SPY points: 5

Date:

COFFEE TO GO

City commuters have grown to love their morning coffee, which many carry from trains and buses into work.

I-SPY points: 5

Date:

SMOOTHIE/JUICE BAR

Freshly made smoothies and juice cocktails are a delicious and healthy alternative to sugary, fizzy drinks.

I-SPY points: 10

Date:

FARMERS' MARKET

Many farmers sell their produce, such as high quality meat, pies, drinks, fruit and vegetables, at small farmers' markets. They are very popular, as people know that they are buying fresh, local produce.

I-SPY points: 10

Date: _____

CAR BOOT SALE

Car boot sales are a great way to pick up bargains – or to sell old toys, DVDs and books that you no longer want.

I-SPY points: 5

Date: _____

SHOPPING MALLS

For many people, the weekend would not be complete without a trip to a giant shopping mall where you can buy almost anything.

I-SPY points: 5

Date: _____

DIY SUPERSTORE

Usually sited on the edge of towns, theses superstores sell garden furniture, plants and do-it-yourself supplies.

I-SPY points: 5

Date: _____

THEME PARKS

A great day out for all the family, from hair raising rides to more sedate attractions.

I-SPY points: 15

Date: _____

ROLLER COASTER

Roller coasters are among the most popular rides at theme parks. High, extremely fast and sometimes terrifying, they're made for thrill-seekers!.

Where is the UK's biggest roller coaster?

I-SPY points: 20

Date: _____

OUTDOOR VIDEO SCREEN

Many cities put up giant outdoor video screens for special events, such as international football matches.

I-SPY points: 20

Date: _____

MULTIPLEX CINEMA

Cinema-goers are spoilt for choice at the average multi-screen cinema.

I-SPY points: 10

Date: _____

JUMBO POPCORN

A trip to the cinema isn't complete without a big box of popcorn.

I-SPY points: 5

Date: _____

AMAZON

Shopping online has become extremely popular. Amazon was launched in 1995 as an online bookseller and is now one of the world's largest online retailers.

I-SPY points: 5

Date: _____

EBAY HOME PAGE

EBay is the world's most famous online auction site. Anyone can use it to sell old stuff or buy just about anything.

I-SPY points: 5

Date: _____

SUPERMARKET DELIVERY VAN

The rise of the Internet has helped supermarkets to develop on-line shopping and home delivery services.

I-SPY points: 10

Date: _____

SUPERMARKET LOYALTY CARD

These cards are electronically swiped at the checkout and regular shoppers can earn discounts and vouchers to save money on future purchases.

I-SPY points: 5

Date: _____

52

SPACE BLANKET

These silver or gold blankets are used by the emergency services or outdoor enthusiasts to provide instant warmth. Lightweight, they can be packed in small spaces, and are often given to marathon runners at the end of races in order to keep warm.

I-SPY points: 10

Date:

CCTV MONITOR

Small security cameras like this are often positioned high on buildings in towns and cities to deter criminals and monitior areas.

I-SPY points: 5

Date:

SECURITY ARCH

This is a kind of metal detector. If a person walks through carrying large pieces of metal on his body, such as a knife, or even large pieces of jewellery, a sensor will be activated, and the person searched.

I-SPY points: 15

Date: _____

X-RAY MACHINE (FOR LUGGAGE)

Special scanning X-ray machines check that passengers on aircraft are safe and are not carrying dangerous items such as guns, knives or explosive items.

I-SPY points: 15

Date: _____

HANDHELD BODY METAL DETECTOR

Handheld wand-shaped scanners can locate exactly where someone is carrying something they shouldn't.

I-SPY points: 15

Date: _____

WIFI HOT SPOT

Log on here to have wireless access to the internet and all your favourite web sites.

I-SPY points: 10

Date: _____

WIFI ZONE

WEB CAMERA

These have many uses, including being able to see your friends whilst chatting on the computer. Be careful. Someone could be watching you!

I-SPY points: 5

Date: _____

BLACKBERRY

Handheld, computers and phones allow instant access to emails or the Internet wherever you are.

I-SPY points: 5

Date: _____

WI-FI ROUTER

Many of us now have more than one computer at home. Wi-Fi routers allow several people to access the internet at once on just one telephone line without lots of wires!.

I-SPY points: 5

Date: _____

BLUETOOTH HEADSET

Bluetooth is a technology that allows electronic devices to communicate wirelessly over a short distance of a few metres. This bluetooth headset allows the user to answer his mobile phone without picking it up or fiddling with the key pad.

I-SPY points: 5

Date: _____

56

Gadgets and Technology

MOBILE PHONE MAST

As the mobile phone network has expanded, these aerials and masts have become a common sight around the country. They relay the electronic signal between phones and operators and are usually seen next to a road.

I-SPY points: 15

Date:

MOBILE PHONE

There are 74 million mobile phones in the UK – that's more than one each for every man, woman and child! How many mobile phones are in your house?

I-SPY points: 5

Date:

IN-CAR DVD PLAYER

Long journeys are less boring if you are lucky enough to have a portable DVD player that can be hooked on to the seat back in front of you.

I-SPY points: 10

Date: _____

SAT NAV

Satellite navigation systems use computer technology and satellites in orbit around the earth to work out where you are and tell you how to get somewhere else.

I-SPY points: 5

Date: _____

LAPTOP COMPUTER

Laptop computers are lightweight and portable, which means that they can provide instant access to work or personal information wherever you are.

I-SPY points: 5

Date: _____

MEMORY STICK

Memory sticks, also known as USB or thumb drives, are the latest in a long line of small electronic devices that allow people to transport documents, pictures and other electronic information from computer to computer.

I-SPY points: 5

Date: _____

FLAT SCREEN TV

Flat panel televisions and computer screens now replace old, cumbersome cathode ray screens. New flat-screen technology means that TV screens can be much larger than traditional televisions and can fit flat on a wall.

I-SPY points: 5

Date: _____

SATELLITE DISH

It's hard to miss these, as there are over 7 million in the UK alone!

I-SPY points: 5

Date: _____

DVD RECORDER

DVD recorders are computer hard disks capable of recording television programmes. They can store many hours of viewing and have superseded the old video recorder with its bulky videotapes.

I-SPY points: 5

Date: _____

IPOD/MP3 PLAYER

MP3 players are one of the great portable inventions, which enable us to carry around thousands of songs on a device the size of small packet of sweets.

I-SPY points: 5

Date: _____

DIGITAL BOOK READER

Digital book readers have not yet become as popular as MP3 players, but the idea behind them means that hundreds of books can be stored on the one device.

I-SPY points: 20

Date: _____

DIGITAL RADIO

Digital radio, which provides crystal-clear sound and a wider choice of radio stations is gradually taking over from the traditional AM/FM radio service.

I-SPY points: 10

Date: _____

DIGITAL CAMERA

Digital photography has made photography more immediate. With a digital camera and a computer, you can share pictures with friends and relations around the world almost almost instantly.

I-SPY points: 5

Date: _____

USB PHOTO FRAME

Hundreds of photos can be stored on digital photo frames. The photo frame then displays them as a slide show, scrolling through the collection of pictures one at a time.

I-SPY points: 10

Date: _____

Index

First published by Michelin Maps and Guides 2010
© Michelin, Propriétaires-Editeurs 2010.
Michelin and the Michelin Man are registered Trademarks of Michelin.
Created and produced by Horizons Publishing Limited.
All rights reserved. No part of this publication may be reproduced, copied or transmitted in any form without the prior consent of the publisher. Print services by FingerPrint International Book production - fingerprint@pandora.be.
The publisher gratefully acknowledges the contribution of the I-Spy team: Judith Millidge, Camilla Lovell, Sheila Watts, Elspeth Walker, Matthew Newman, Ian Bell and Ruth Neilson in the production of this title.
The publisher gratefully acknowledges the contribution and assistance of all the sites and attractions in the book, plus Bill Boaden, unitaw, The Eden Project, Hanan Smart, Sian Iddiols, Justin Perkins, Tom Bell, Anthony Thomas, B&Q Stores, Alton Towers, Tesco Stores Ltd, Andrew Barrow, Britain on View, visitcardiff.com, James Huckle, London 2012 Organising Committee, Eurostar, Steve Parker, Paul Proctor, Transport for London, Dr Karel Hladky, Kevin Abele, John Marchant, Kendra Coupland, Simon Baddeley, Greenshooots Photography, Glyn Kirk - Getty Images, Scott Beale and David Boardman who provided the photographs in this book. Other images in the public domain and used under a creative commons license. All logos, images designs and image rights are © the copyright holders and are used with thanks and kind permission.

HOW TO GET YOUR I-SPY CERTIFICATE AND BADGE

Every time you score 1000 points or more in an I-Spy book, you can apply for a certificate

HERE'S WHAT TO DO, STEP BY STEP:

Certificate

- Ask an adult to check your score
- Ask his or her permission to apply for a certificate
- Apply online to www.ispymichelin.com
- Enter your name and address and the completed title
- We will send you back via e mail your certificate for the title

Badge

- Each I-Spy title has a cut out (page corner) token at the back of the book
- Collect five tokens from different I-Spy titles
- Put Second Class Stamps on two strong envelopes
- Write your own address on one envelope and put a £1 coin inside it (for protection). Fold, but do not seal the envelope, and place it inside the second envelope
- Write the following address on the second envelope, seal it carefully and post to:

I-Spy Books
Michelin Maps and Guides
Hannay House
39 Clarendon Road
Watford
WD17 1JA

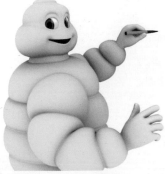